Theory Paper Grade 1 2017 A

Duration 1½ hours

CW00338512

Candidates should answer ALL questions.
Write your answers on this paper – no others will be accepted.
Answers must be written clearly and neatly – otherwise marks may be lost.

TOTAL MARKS
100

1 Add the missing bar-lines to these two melodies. The first bar-line is given in each.

10

2 (a) Draw a circle around the **higher** note of each of these pairs of notes.

10

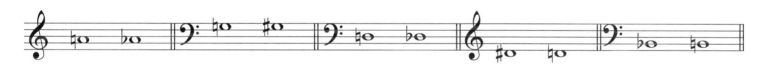

(b) Draw a circle around the **lower** note of each of these pairs of notes.

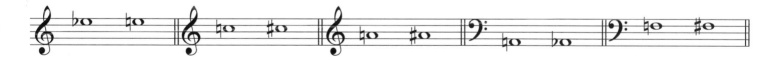

3 Using semibreves (whole notes), write one octave of the scales named below. `10`
Do **not** use key signatures, but remember to add any necessary accidentals.

C major, ascending

F major, descending

4 Answer **both** (a) and (b). `10`

(a) Add the correct clef to each of these tonic triads.

G major   D major

Letter names   ....

(b) Under each triad write the letter name of each note, including the sharp sign where necessary.

5 Next to each note write a rest that has the same time value, as shown in the first answer. `10`

4

6 Give the number (e.g. 2nd, 3rd, 4th) of each of these melodic intervals, as shown in the first answer. The key is C major.

[10]

6th
....

....

....

....

....

....

7 Answer **both** (a) and (b).

[10]

(a) Name the degree of the scale (e.g. 2nd, 3rd, 4th) of each of the notes marked *, as shown in the first answer. The key is F major.

Rossini

5th
....

(b) Give the letter name of the **lowest** note in the melody. ....

8 Tick one box for each term/sign, as shown in the first answer.

[10]

accelerando means:

gradually getting quicker	✔
gradually getting slower	☐
gradually getting louder	☐
gradually getting quieter	☐

Andante means:

quick	☐
at a medium speed	☐
slow	☐
gradually getting slower	☐

cantabile means:

slow	☐
smoothly	☐
in a singing style	☐
gradually getting quieter	☐

means:

slur: detached	☐
tie: hold for the value of both notes	☐
tie: detached	☐
slur: perform smoothly	☐

means:

gradually getting louder	☐
accent the note	☐
gradually getting quieter	☐
gradually getting quicker	☐

mp means:

quiet	☐
moderately quiet	☐
moderately loud	☐
very quiet	☐

9 Look at this melody, which is adapted from a piece by Mendelssohn, and then answer the questions below.

Write your answer to question (b) on the stave below.

(a) (i) Give the time name (e.g. minim or
half note) of the **longest rest** in the melody. ....

10

(ii) How many semiquavers (16th notes) is the last note of the melody worth? ....

(iii) Answer TRUE or FALSE to these sentences:

$\frac{2}{4}$ means two crotchet (quarter-note) beats in a bar. ....

All the notes in bar 5 can be found in the key of D major. ....

(iv) Give the letter name of the third note in bar 7
(marked *), including the sharp sign if necessary. ....

(b) Copy out the music from the start of bar 1 to the end of bar 4, exactly as it is written
above. Don't forget the clef, key signature, time signature, tempo marking, dynamic
and all other details. Write the music on the blank stave above question (a).

10

Theory Paper   Grade 1   2017   B

Duration 1½ hours

TOTAL MARKS
100

Candidates should answer ALL questions.
Write your answers on this paper – no others will be accepted.
Answers must be written clearly and neatly – otherwise marks may be lost.

1 (a) Add the time signature to each of these three examples.

10

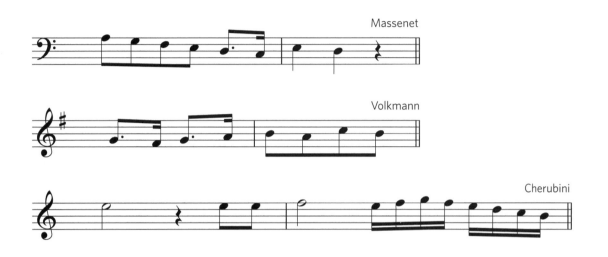

(b) Add a rest at each of the two places marked ∗ to make the bars complete.

2 Write the dynamics *ff p mf pp mp f* in the correct order, from the **quietest** to the **loudest**. The first answer is given.

10

pp

....

3 (a) Draw a circle around the **higher** note of each of these pairs of notes.

(b) Draw a circle around the **lower** note of each of these pairs of notes.

4 Add the correct clef to make each of these named notes, as shown in the first answer.

D

A

B

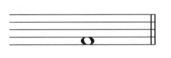

F

middle C

F#

G

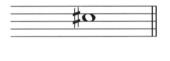

C#

B♭

E

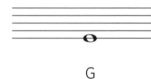

G

5 Answer **both** (a) and (b).

(a) Give the letter name of each of the notes marked ∗, including the sharp sign where necessary. The first answer is given.

Gounod

G

....

(b) Give the time name (e.g. minim or half note) of the rest marked ↓. ....

6 Name the major keys shown by these key signatures. The first answer is given.

G major

....

....

....

....

....

....

7 Rewrite the following melody, grouping (beaming) the notes correctly.

Haydn (adapted)

8 Tick one box for each term/sign, as shown in the first answer.

Lento means:

smoothly	☐
gradually getting slower	☐
at a medium speed	☐
slow	✔

Allegretto means:

slow	☐
fairly quick	☐
gradually getting quicker	☐
gradually getting slower	☐

p means:

quiet	☐
very quiet	☐
moderately quiet	☐
moderately loud	☐

cresc. means:

gradually getting slower	☐
gradually getting quicker	☐
gradually getting louder	☐
gradually getting quieter	☐

accelerando means:

accent the note	☐
fairly quick	☐
gradually getting louder	☐
gradually getting quicker	☐

means:

staccato: detached	☐
accent the note	☐
gradually getting quieter	☐
legato: smoothly	☐

9

9 Look at this melody by C. Loewe and then answer the questions below.

Write your answer to question (b) on the stave below.

(a) (i)   How many bars contain a quaver (eighth-note) rest?   ....

   (ii)   Complete this sentence:

       Bar 3 has the same notes and rhythm as bar ....

   (iii) This melody is in the key of G major. Name the degree of
       the scale (e.g. 4th, 5th, 6th) of the first note in bar 4 (marked ∗).   ....

   (iv) Answer TRUE or FALSE to this sentence:

       Bar 1 contains **all** the notes of the tonic triad of G major.   ....

   (v)   How many semiquavers (16th notes) is the last note of the melody worth?   ....

(b) Copy out the music from the start of bar 1 to the end of bar 2, exactly as it is written
    above. Don't forget the clef, key signature, time signature, tempo marking, dynamics
    and all other details. Write the music on the blank stave above question (a).

Theory Paper   Grade 1   2017   C

Duration 1½ hours

TOTAL MARKS
100

Candidates should answer ALL questions.
Write your answers on this paper – no others will be accepted.
Answers must be written clearly and neatly – otherwise marks may be lost.

1 (a) Add the time signature to each of these three examples.

10

(b) Add the missing bar-lines to this melody. The first bar-line is given.

2 Name the major key of each of these tonic triads, as shown in the first answer.

10

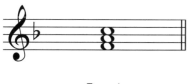

F major
....

....

....

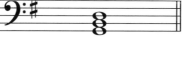

....

....

....

3 Add a rest at the places marked * in these two melodies to make each bar complete.

Cherubini

Rossini (adapted)

4 Add the correct clef to make each of these named notes, as shown in the first answer.

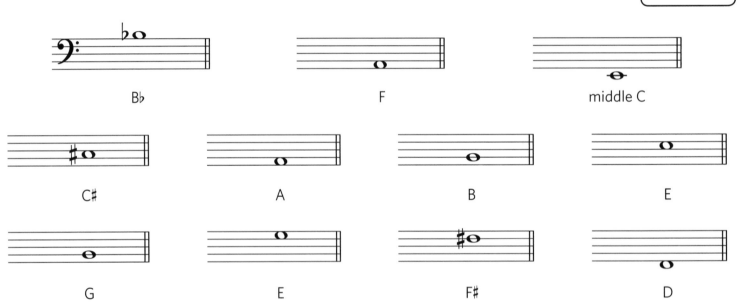

Bb   F   middle C

C#   A   B   E

G   E   F#   D

5 Name the key of each of these scales. Also draw a bracket (⌐⎯⌐) over each pair of notes making a semitone, as shown in the first scale.

Key ....

Key ....

Key ....

6 Answer **both** (a) and (b).

> 10

(a) Name the degree of the scale (e.g. 2nd, 3rd, 4th) of each of the notes marked *, as shown in the first answer. The key is D major.

Shield

7th ....

(b) Give the letter name of the first note of the melody, including the sharp sign if necessary. ....

7 **After** each note write a **higher** note to form the named **melodic** interval within the key of F major. The first answer is given.

> 10

6th   2nd   4th

8th / 8ve   7th   5th

8 Tick one box for each term/sign, as shown in the first answer.

> 10

a tempo means:

held back ☐
in time ✔
the end ☐
a little ☐

♩ = 48 means:

48 crotchet beats ☐
48 crotchet notes ☐
48 crotchet beats in a minute ☐
48 crotchets in the melody ☐

cantabile means:

at a medium speed ☐
slow ☐
repeat from the beginning ☐
in a singing style ☐

Adagio means:

slow ☐
held back ☐
gradually getting slower ☐
fairly quick ☐

means:

tie: hold for the value of both notes ☐
slur: detached ☐
tie: detached ☐
slur: perform smoothly ☐

means:

gradually getting quicker ☐
gradually getting quieter ☐
gradually getting louder ☐
gradually getting slower ☐

13

9 Look at this melody, which is adapted from a piece by Burgmüller, and then answer the questions below.

Write your answer to question (b) on the stave below.

(a) (i) Give the time name (e.g. crotchet or
quarter note) of the **longest** note in the melody. ....

(ii) Give the number of a bar that contains
two notes next to each other that are a 3rd apart.   Bar ....

(iii) Answer TRUE or FALSE to these sentences:

The **4** in $\frac{2}{4}$ means crotchet (quarter-note) beats. ....

All the notes in bars 7–8 can be found in the key of F major.   ....

(iv) Give the letter name of the **lowest** note in the melody.   ....

(b) Copy out the music from the start of bar 5 to the end of bar 8, exactly as it is written   [10]
above. Don't forget the clef, key signature, dynamics and all other details. Write the
music on the blank stave above question (a).

Theory Paper   Grade 1   2017   S

Duration 1½ hours

Candidates should answer ALL questions.
Write your answers on this paper – no others will be accepted.
Answers must be written clearly and neatly – otherwise marks may be lost.

TOTAL MARKS
100

1 (a) Add the time signature to each of these three examples.

10

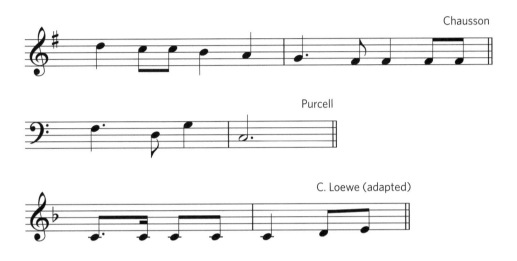

(b) Add a rest at each of the two places marked * to make the bars complete.

2 Write the dynamics *pp mp f mf p ff* in the correct order, from the **loudest** to the **quietest**. The first answer is given.

10

3 Name the major key of each of these tonic triads, as shown in the first answer.

10

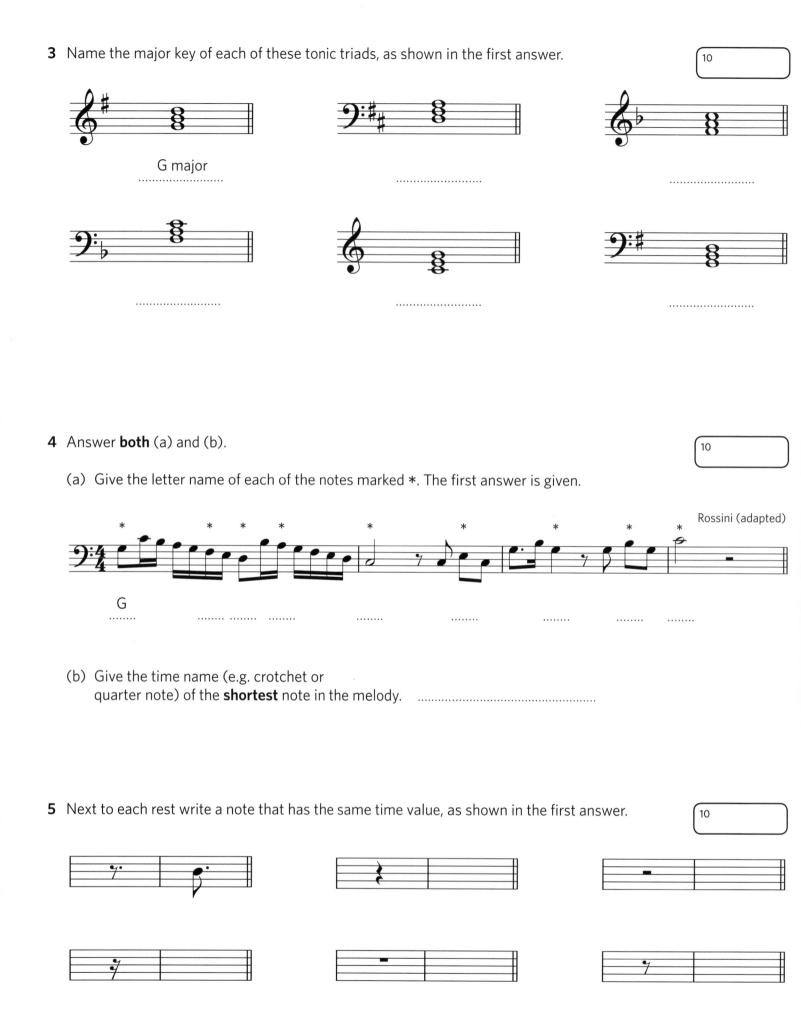

G major

....

....

....

....

....

....

4 Answer **both** (a) and (b).

10

(a) Give the letter name of each of the notes marked *. The first answer is given.

Rossini (adapted)

G

....

(b) Give the time name (e.g. crotchet or quarter note) of the **shortest** note in the melody.   ....

5 Next to each rest write a note that has the same time value, as shown in the first answer.

10

6 Add the correct clef and any necessary accidentals to make each of the scales named below. Do **not** use key signatures.

C major

F major

10

7 Give the number (e.g. 2nd, 3rd, 4th) of each of these harmonic intervals, as shown in the first answer. The key is G major.

10

6th

....

....

....

....

....

....

8 Tick one box for each term/sign, as shown in the first answer.

10

8va------------⌐ means:

perform the notes smoothly	☐
perform an octave lower	☐
pause on the note or rest	☐
perform an octave higher	✔

Allegro means:

fairly quick	☐
quick	☐
at a medium speed	☐
slow	☐

ritardando (rit.) means:

gradually getting slower	☐
gradually getting quieter	☐
slow	☐
gradually getting louder	☐

f means:

very loud	☐
loud	☐
gradually getting louder	☐
moderately loud	☐

means:

slur: perform smoothly	☐
tie: detached	☐
slur: detached	☐
tie: hold for the value of both notes	☐

means:

staccato: detached	☐
legato: smoothly	☐
accent the note	☐
gradually getting quieter	☐

9 Look at this melody by Grieg and then answer the questions below.

Write your answer to question (b) on the stave below.

(a) (i) How many bars contain a dotted crotchet (dotted quarter-note)? ....

(ii) How many semiquavers (16th notes) is the rest in the last bar worth? ....

(iii) Underline one of the following words that describes how the first two notes of bar 5 should be played.

legato (smoothly)   or   *staccato* (detached)

(iv) This melody is in the key of G major. Name the degree of the scale (e.g. 2nd, 3rd, 4th) of the last note of the melody. ....

(v) Give the number of a bar that contains **all** the notes of the tonic triad of G major.   Bar ....

(b) Copy out the music from the start of bar 1 to the end of bar 3, exactly as it is written above. Don't forget the clef, key signature, time signature, tempo marking, dynamic and all other details. Write the music on the blank stave above question (a).

Music Theory Practice Papers 2017

ABRSM's official Music Theory Practice Papers are essential resources for candidates preparing for our Music Theory exams. They provide authentic practice materials and a reliable guide to what to expect in the exam.

Key features:

- Four separate papers adapted from ABRSM's 2017 Music Theory exams for Grade 1
- Includes new question types in use from 2018
- Model answers also available

Support material for ABRSM Music Theory exams

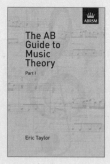

Supporting the teaching and learning of music in partnership with the Royal Schools of Music

Royal Academy of Music | Royal College of Music
Royal Northern College of Music | Royal Conservatoire of Scotland

www.abrsm.org   f facebook.com/abrsm
🐦 @abrsm   ▶ ABRSM YouTube

ISBN 978-1-78601-076-6

9 781786 010766